My World

People Who Help Us

C000220243

* Especially suitable for early years

Introduction

The  series of books is a brand new collection of topic-based songbooks. Each includes twelve easy-to-learn and catchy songs by some of Britain's most popular children's songwriters. The accompanying CD features all songs sung by children along with professionally produced backing tracks.

Developed specifically for pre-school and reception aged children, we feel that the music and topics covered will also be particularly appropriate for use with children up to the age of around seven. The songs can be used to supplement the 'creative' requirements of the foundation stage, as well as contributing to many other areas of the curriculum. Each lyric page contains helpful teacher's notes to expand and develop the subject content of the songs.

In addition to the teaching ideas given with each song, we suggest adding some simple percussion using instruments available in the classroom, and perhaps some homemade ones. It's important that children relate to music as something that they can become actively involved with and enjoy. Using percussion and easy clapping rhythms gives everyone a chance to really join in.

The Dustbin Men

Words and Music by Mark and Helen Johnson
CCLI Song No. 4270584

1. The dustbin men are coming,
    To take away the rubbish.
    Our kitchen bins are full to the brim,
    With sprouts and rotten cabbage!

    So bag it up! Clear it out!
    Throw it all away!
    And don't forget that the dustbin men,
    Are coming today!

2. The dustbin men are coming,
    To take away the rubbish.
    Our kitchen bins are full to the brim,
    With soggy fruit and salad!

    CHORUS

3. The dustbin men are coming,
    To take away the rubbish.
    Our kitchen bins are full to the brim,
    With bags and sticky wrappers!

    CHORUS

    And don't forget that the dustbin men,
    Are coming today!

Every household creates lots of rubbish and waste. Can the children think of different sorts of rubbish that they throw away in their home?

Talk about recycling waste and why this is important to protect our environment. What sorts of things we can recycle – glass, paper, textiles, books, etc? Set up a 'paper' bin in the classroom for the children to put their waste paper in. Perhaps you could make different children responsible for emptying this at the end of each day.

Lollipop Lady

Words and Music by Niki Davies
CCLI Song No. 4270601

1. Who has a bright coat? Who has a hat?
    Who has a smile as wide as that?
    Lollipop Lady, Lollipop Lady,
    It's the Lollipop Lady.

2. Who holds a stick with a circle on top?
    Who can make the traffic stop?
    Lollipop Lady, Lollipop Lady,
    It's the Lollipop Lady.

3. She makes it safe to cross the street,
    Then off we go with our busy feet,
    Lollipop Lady, Lollipop Lady,
    It's the Lollipop Lady.

    Lollipop Lady, Lollipop Lady,
    It's the Lollipop Lady.

Do any of the children see a Lollipop Lady on their way to nursery or school – or perhaps on the way to an older brother's or sister's school?

Why do we need Lollipop Ladies? Can the children think of other safe places to cross the road? What should they do every time they need to cross a road?

Create a game to play whilst you're singing this song: dress one of the children up as the 'Lollipop Lady' – make a paper hat and use a cardboard tube with a circle on top for the stick. During the first two lines of each verse, the other children should wait at the side of 'the road', then during the "Lollipop Lady" lyrics, they should take turns to cross the road. The children will begin to learn to wait their turn, whilst listening to the lyrics and doing simple actions as they are singing.

Who Is There For Me?

Words and Music by Ann Beresford
CCLI Song No. 4270618

1. Who is there for me when I've fallen down?
    Who is there for me when I've been a clown?
    Who is there for me when I wear a frown?
    Who is there to help me most?
    My family!

    They're the ones who know me best,
    Love me when I've been a pest,
    I love them and they love me,
    My family!

2. Who is there for me if I'm asking "Why"?
    Who is there for me if I'm asking "How"?
    Who is there for me if I'm asking "When"?
    Who is there to help me most?
    My family!

    CHORUS

3. Who is there for me when I'm feeling grumpy?
    Who is there for me when I'm feeling happy?
    Who is there for me when I'm feeling sorry?
    Who is there to help me most?
    My family!

    CHORUS

Families come in all shapes and sizes. Get the children to talk about their families. Do they have brothers or sisters, Grannies or Great-Grannies and so on? How do their families help them do everyday things?

Ask the children to draw a picture of their family.

Going To The Doctor's

Words and Music by Sha Armstrong
CCLI Song No. 4270625

1. Mummy's taking me to the doctor's today,
    I've got a cold and it won't go away,
    She said he's going to give me medicine to take,
    To make me feel much better.
    A-a-a-choo! Mummy I am afraid,
    A-chooo! I don't like medicine,
    But my cold won't go away.

2. Mummy's taking me to the doctor's today,
    I've got a cough and it won't go away,
    She said he's going to give me medicine to take,
    To make me feel much better.
    Cough, cough! Mummy I am afraid,
    Cough! I don't like medicine,
    But my cough won't go away.

3. Mummy's taking me to the doctor's today,
    I've got the flu and it won't go away,
    She said he's going to give me medicine to take,
    To make me feel much better.
    Moan, moan! Mummy I am afraid,
    Oh! I don't like medicine,
    But my flu won't go away.

4. One, two, three, four,
    Five days later and I'm feeling OK,
    My cold and cough's gone and the flu flew away,
    So next time I won't be afraid,
    The doctor made me better!

Can the children think of anyone else that might help when you're feeling a bit poorly – nurses, dentists, etc? Talk about where they work, for example some doctors work in hospitals whilst others work in a local surgery. Have any of the children been to a hospital – perhaps to visit when a baby sister or brother was born?

If you find this song quite tricky for younger children to sing, try getting them to play along with simple percussion instruments, and joining in with the sneezing, coughing and moaning!

My Teacher

Words and Music by Niki Davies
CCLI Song No. 4270632

1. My teacher taught me how to count,
   How to count, how to count.
   My teacher taught me how to count,
   One, two, three, four, five,
   One, two, three, four, five.

2. My teacher taught me the alphabet,
   The alphabet, the alphabet.
   My teacher taught me the alphabet,
   A, B, C, D, E,
   A, B, C, D, E.

3. My teacher taught me how to paint,
   How to paint, how to paint.
   My teacher taught me how to paint,
   With red and green and blue,
   With red and green and blue.

4. My teacher taught me left and right,
   Left and right, left and right.
   My teacher taught me left and right,
   My left arm and my right,
   My left arm and my right.

5. My teacher taught me how to dance,
   How to dance, how to dance.
   My teacher taught me how to dance,
   So dance along with me,
   So dance along with me.

This is a great song for actions. Use fingers for counting one to five and A to E, extravagant 'brush strokes' for the painting verse, your left and right arms for verse four, and use the instrumental section at the end of the song for the children to show how well they can dance.

It's The Window Cleaner!

Words and Music by Mark and Helen Johnson
CCLI Song No. 4270649

1. Who comes along,
   With a ladder and a van?
   A ladder and a van,
   And a bucket in his hand?
   Who comes along,
   With a ladder and a van?
   Say "Hello!", it's the window cleaner!

2. Who does the job,
   With a squeegee and a mop?
   A squeegee and a mop,
   And a special kind of cloth?
   Who does the job,
   With a squeegee and a mop?
   Say "Hello!", it's the window cleaner!

3. Who can we please,
   With a lovely cup of tea?
   A lovely cup of tea,
   With a biscuit for a treat?
   Who can we please,
   With a lovely cup of tea?
   Say "Hello!", it's the window cleaner!

The window cleaner uses lots of different things to help clean the windows. What else do we use around the house to help keep it clean, such as dusters, vacuum cleaners, dish clothes, dustpan and brush etc. What do we use to clean ourselves?

The Firefighter's Song

Words and Music by Ann Beresford
CCLI Song No. 4270656

I am a firefighter,
I wear a yellow hat,
And when the bell rings you can tell,
There's a fire to put out.
So down the pole I slide so fast,
And off in the engine I go,
Racing through the traffic with my siren blowing so ...

Nee-naw, nee-naw, nee-naw, nee-naw,
Now unwind the hose,
Nee-naw, nee-naw, nee-naw, nee-naw,
Up the ladders we go,
Nee-naw, nee-naw, nee-naw, nee-naw,
Spray the water on,
Rescue all the people,
Until the fire's gone!

Repeat whole song

This is a great song for some music and movement! Use the chorus to act out the words and really let rip on the 'nee-naws'!

Talk about fire and why it can be dangerous. Do any of the children have a fire in their living rooms? Why is it there? Does it keep the room warm or cold? Why shouldn't they 'touch' the fire?

Talk about other things that are hot – drinks, radiators, hot taps, etc. What else can the children think of that they should avoid touching, for example things that are sharp or fragile?

The Hairdresser Song

Words and Music by Sha Armstrong

CCLI Song No. 4272908

1. I can't, I can't see,
    My eyes are covered up with hair,
    It's time for, time for me,
    To take a trip to you know where, you know where!

    The scissors go snip, snip, snip again,
    I count five, six, seven, eight, nine, ten.
    The scissors go snip, snip, snip some more,
    My hair comes off, falls on the floor.

2. Well I must sit, must sit still,
    Look straight ahead, don't turn around,
    But I feel, I feel ill,
    As I see my hair lying on the ground, on the ground.

    CHORUS

3. But now I can, I can see,
    I look in the mirror and the job's well done,
    I do b-, I do believe,
    A trip to the hairdresser's can be fun, can be fun,
    Well it's such fun when ...

    CHORUS x 2

This song deals with a subject that can be quite difficult for some younger children. It might be strange for them to see all their hair coming off when they first go to the hairdresser's and it's also very difficult to sit still!

Look at the different types of hair that the children have in the group. Count how many have long hair, short hair, brown, black or blonde hair and so on.

This might be a tricky song for younger children to sing, but they can all join in the chorus, especially the counting on from five.

Special Friend

Words and Music by Margaret Carpenter
CCLI Song No. 4272915

1. I've got a special friend,
   Who loves me, loves me,
   If I am feeling down,
   He always makes me smile.

   If I'm away he'll always say,
   "I'm glad you're back today".
   I love my friend it's true,
   And everyone knows,
   Surely it shows,
   Everyone knows it's you.

2. I've got a special friend,
   Who loves me, loves me,
   If I am feeling down,
   She always makes me smile.

   If I'm away she'll always say,
   "I'm glad you're back today".
   I love my friend it's true,
   And everyone knows,
   Surely it shows,
   Everyone knows it's you.

What makes a friend special? Talk about feelings: can the children think of things that make them feel happy - and what makes them feel sad? Talk about things you can do to make other people happy, and how it's easier to make a friend by being a friend.

Perhaps they could think of something to do for someone else today that would make that person smile.

The Postman

Words and Music by Niki Davies
CCLI Song No. 4272922

1. It's raining, it's raining,
    It's raining everywhere!
    But the postman doesn't care,
    He still gets the letters to you, oh yeah!
    He still gets the letters to you.

2. It's snowing, it's snowing,
    It's snowing everywhere!
    But the postman doesn't care,
    He still gets the letters to you, oh yeah!
    He still gets the letters to you.

3. It's windy, it's windy,
    It's windy everywhere!
    But the postman doesn't care,
    He still gets the letters to you, oh yeah!
    He still gets the letters to you.

4. It's foggy, it's foggy,
    It's foggy everywhere!
    But the postman doesn't care,
    He still gets the letters to you, oh yeah!
    He still gets the letters to you.

Talk about communication and that letters are a form of this. What other forms of communication can the children think of? (Email, speech, sign language, TV, radio, and so on.) Which of these do they use?

Get the children to draw a picture on a postcard and write their name underneath. With a little help, they can address the postcard to themselves, add a stamp and put it in the postbox. What do they think will happen to the postcard next?

The Plumber Song

Words and Music by Alison Hedger
CCLI Song No. 4272939

I'm a qualified plumber,
Here to help with my bag of tools.
You can watch and copy,
All the things I've learnt to do.

1. Push the pipes in, *(push the pipes in)*,
   Stop the dripping, *(stop the dripping)*,
   Flush the new loo, *(flush the new loo)*,
   No more pools when I've used my tools!

CHORUS

2. Clear the drainpipe, *(clear the drainpipe)*,
   Free the plughole, *(free the plughole)*,
   Screw the tap back, *(screw the tap back)*,
   No more pools when I've used my tools!

CHORUS

3. Fix the boiler, *(fix the boiler)*,
   Set the timer, *(set the timer)*,
   Turn the heat on, *(turn the heat on)*,
   No more pools when I've used my tools!

CHORUS

Plumbers are just one of many types of people who fix problems in our homes. Talk about similar professions and what their jobs involve, for example, electricians, builders, chimney sweeps and so on.

Have any of the children had people in their house to do jobs and help fix things?

Can I Help You?

Words and Music by Mark and Helen Johnson
CCLI Song No. 4272946

1. Can I help you? Can I help you?
    Tell me if there's anything I can do.
    Can I help you? Can I help you?
    Maybe I could carry a bag or two?

2. Can I help you? Can I help you?
    Tell me if there's anything I can do.
    Can I help you? Can I help you?
    Maybe I could open the door for you?

3. Can I help you? Can I help you?
    Tell me if there's anything I can do.
    Can I help you? Can I help you?
    Maybe I could tidy my room with you?

4. Can I help you? Can I help you?
    Tell me if there's anything I can do.
    Can I help you? Can I help you?
    Maybe I could sweep up the floor for you?

5. Can I help you? Can I help you?
    Tell me if there's anything I can do.
    Can I help you? Can I help you?
    Maybe I could empty the bins with you?

We've talked about lots of people who help us, but what can we do to help others and make their lives easier? Why not try making up some more verses to the song with all the things you think of?

The Dustbin Men

Words & Music by
Mark and Helen Johnson

1. The
2. The
3. The

dust - bin men are com - ing to take a - way the
dust - bin men are com - ing to take a - way the
dust - bin men are com - ing to take a - way the

rub - bish. Our kit - chen bins are full to the brim with
rub - bish. Our kit - chen bins are full to the brim with
rub - bish. Our kit - chen bins are full to the brim with

Lollipop Lady

Words & Music by
Niki Davies

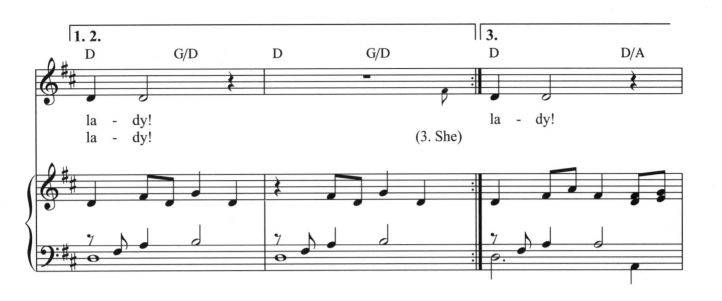

la - dy!
la - dy!
la - dy!
(3. She)

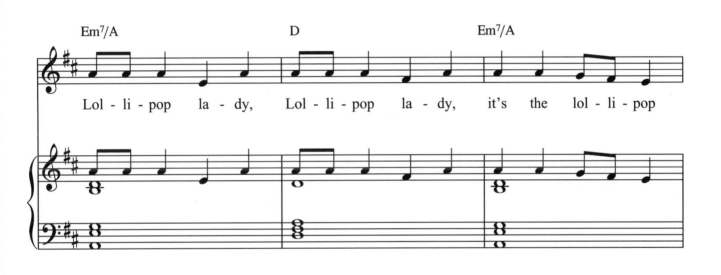

Lol - li - pop la - dy, Lol - li - pop la - dy, it's the lol - li - pop

poco rit.

la - dy!

Who Is There For Me?

Words & Music by
Ann Beresford

With flowing movement ♩ = 150

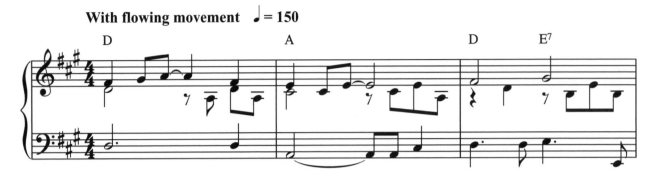

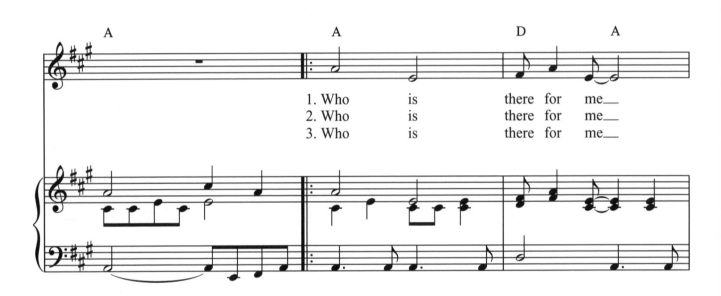

1. Who is there for me
2. Who is there for me
3. Who is there for me

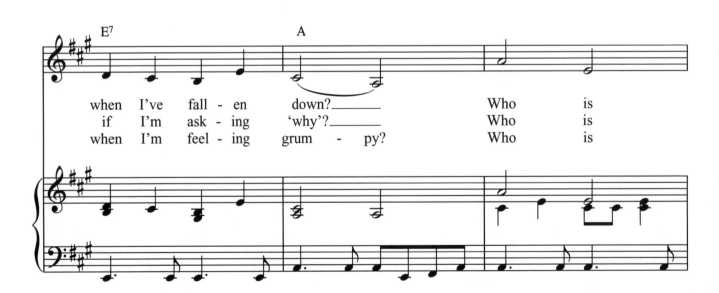

when I've fall - en down? Who is
if I'm ask - ing 'why'? Who is
when I'm feel - ing grum - py? Who is

there for me___ when I've been a clown?_____
there for me___ if I'm ask - ing 'how'?_____
there for me___ when I'm feel - ing hap - py?

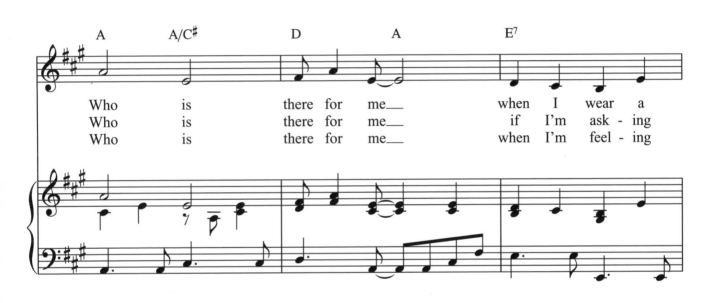

Who is there for me___ when I wear a
Who is there for me___ if I'm ask - ing
Who is there for me___ when I'm feel - ing

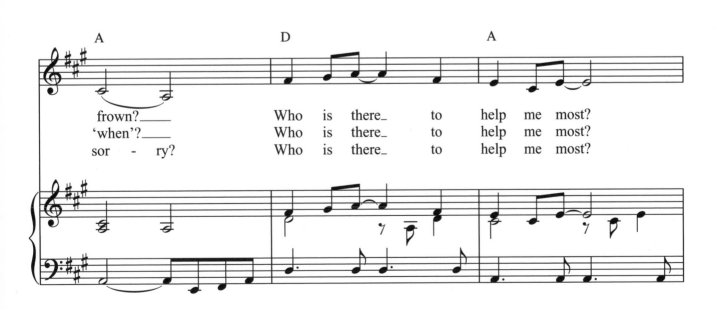

frown?___ Who is there_ to help me most?
'when'?___ Who is there_ to help me most?
sor - ry? Who is there_ to help me most?

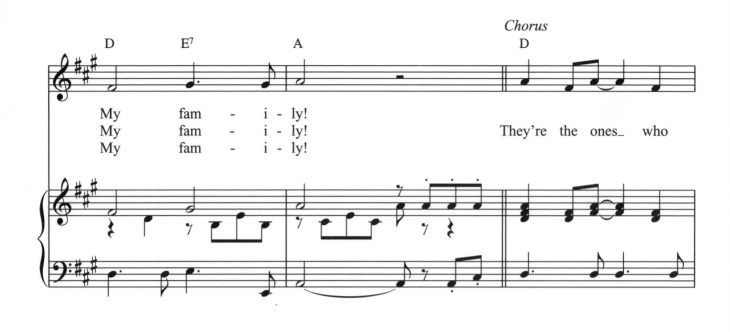

My fam - i - ly!
My fam - i - ly!
My fam - i - ly!   They're the ones_ who

know me best,_   love me when I've   been a pest,_   I love them and

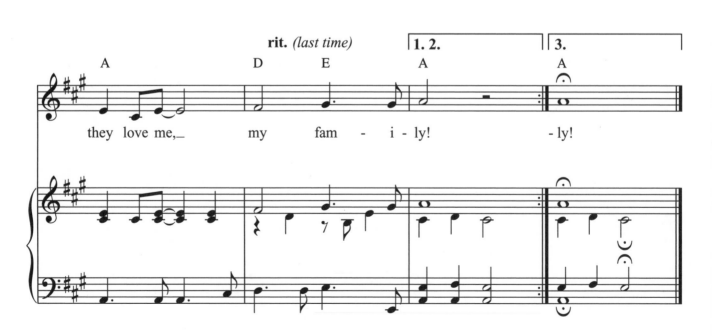

they love me,_   my fam - i - ly!   - ly!

Going To The Doctor's

Words & Music by
Sha Armstrong

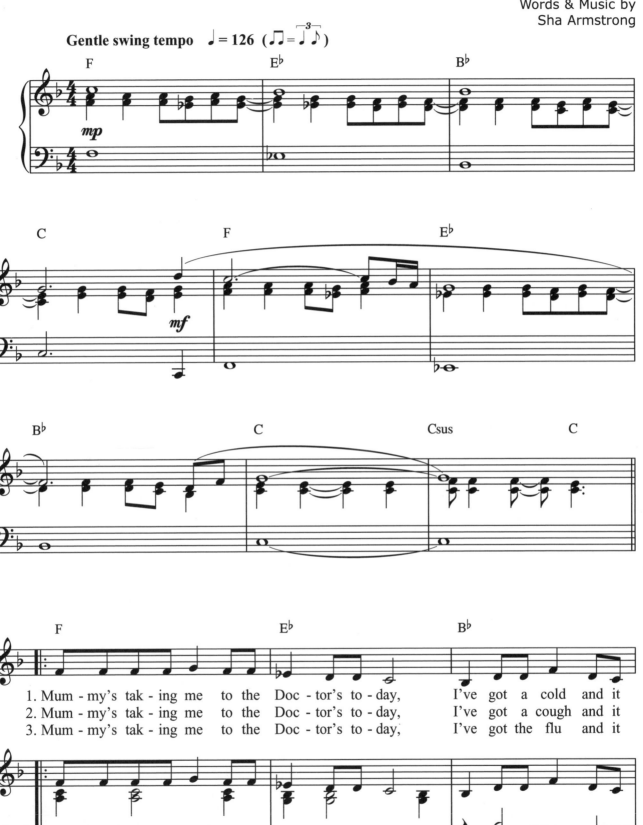

1. Mum - my's tak - ing me to the Doc - tor's to - day, I've got a cold and it
2. Mum - my's tak - ing me to the Doc - tor's to - day, I've got a cough and it
3. Mum - my's tak - ing me to the Doc - tor's to - day, I've got the flu and it

1. 2.   3.

1, 2, 3, 4

Five days la - ter and I'm feel - ing o - kay,   my cold and cough's gone and the

flu flew a - way!   So next time I won't be a - fraid, the

Doc - tor made me bet - ter!_____

rit.

My Teacher

Words & Music by
Niki Davies

It's The Window Cleaner!

Words & Music by
Mark and Helen Johnson

With a cheery feel ♩ = 120

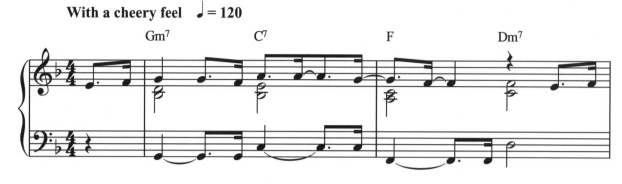

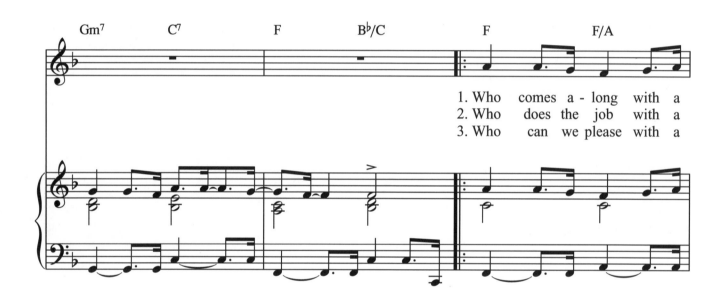

1. Who comes a - long with a
2. Who does the job with a
3. Who can we please with a

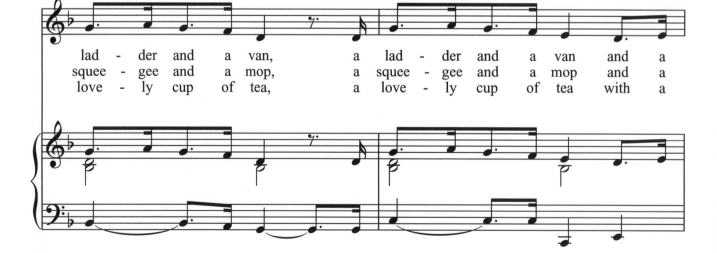

lad - der and a van, a lad - der and a van and a
squee - gee and a mop, a squee - gee and a mop and a
love - ly cup of tea, a love - ly cup of tea with a

buck - et in his hand?
spe - cial kind of cloth?
bis - cuit for a treat?

Who comes a - long with a
Who does the job with a
Who can we please with a

lad - der and a van? Say "hel - lo!", it's the win - dow___ clean-
squee - gee and a mop? Say "hel - lo!", it's the win - dow___ clean-
love - ly cup of tea? Say "hel - lo!", it's the win - dow___ clean-

1. 2.

- er!___
- er!___

3.

- er!___ Say "hel - lo!", it's the win - dow___ clean - er!___

29

The Firefighter's Song

Words & Music by
Ann Beresford

Lively, staccato feel ♩ = 80

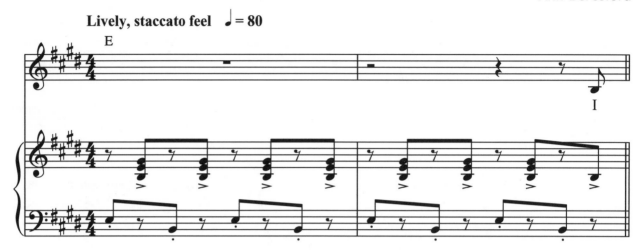

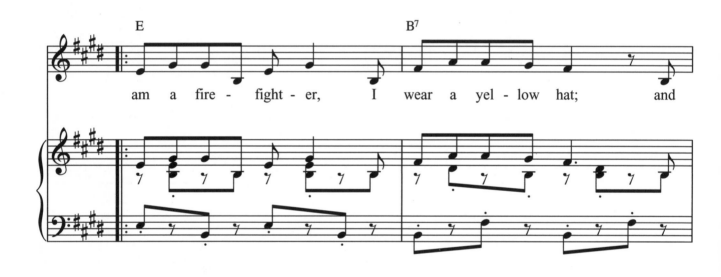

am a fire-fight-er, I wear a yel-low hat; and

when the bell rings you can tell there's a fi-re to put out! So

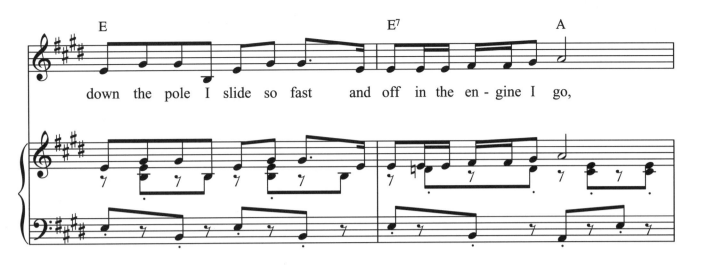

down the pole I slide so fast and off in the en-gine I go,

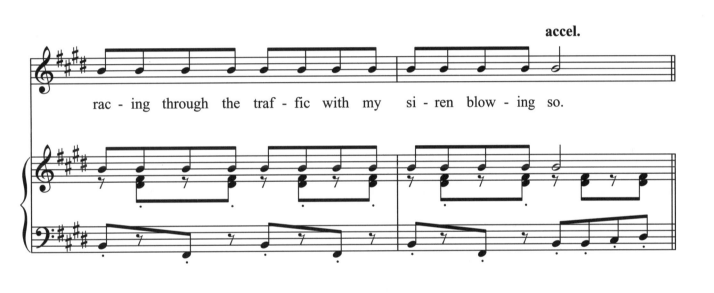

accel.

rac-ing through the traf-fic with my si-ren blow-ing so.

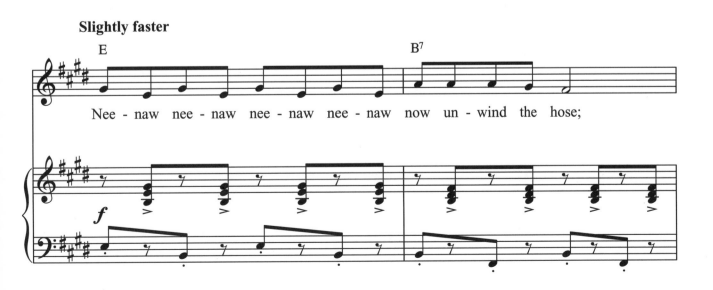

Slightly faster

Nee-naw nee-naw nee-naw nee-naw now un-wind the hose;

neenaw neenaw neenaw neenaw up the ladders we go!

Neenaw neenaw neenaw neenaw spray the water on,

rescue all the people until the fire's gone!

The Hairdresser Song

Words & Music by
Sha Armstrong

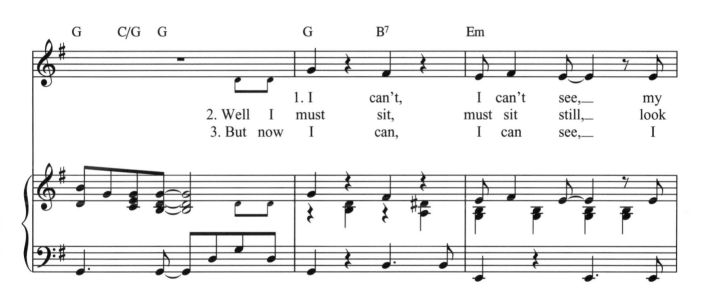

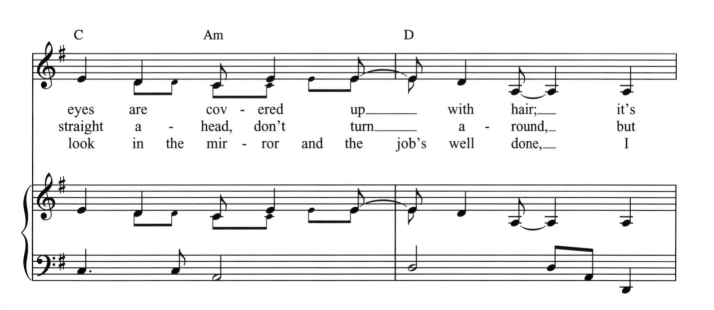

33

Special Friend

Words & Music by
Margaret Carpenter

Gently ♩ = 100

I've got a spe - cial friend who loves me, loves me. If I am feel - ing down he al - ways makes me (2. she)

smile. If I'm a - way he'll al - ways say "I'm (2. she'll)

The Postman

Words & Music by
Niki Davies

Bouncy swing feel ♩ = 148

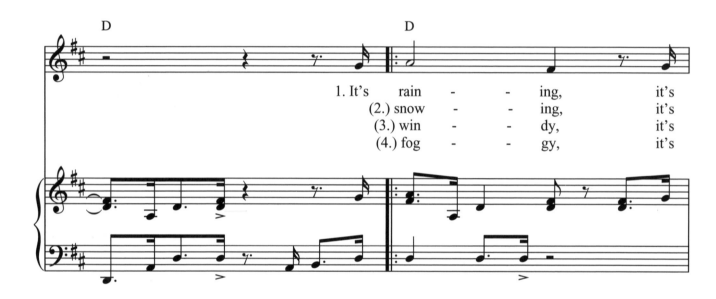

1. It's rain - - ing, it's
(2.) snow - - ing, it's
(3.) win - - dy, it's
(4.) fog - - gy, it's

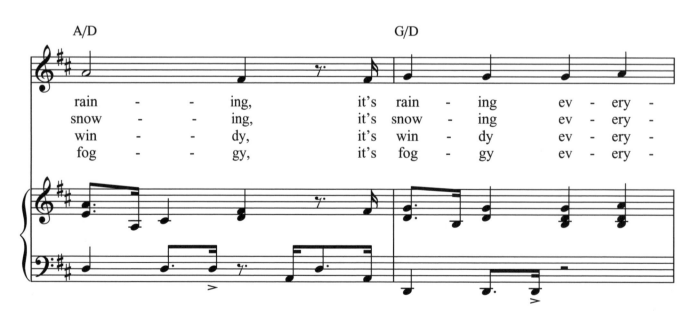

rain - - ing, it's rain - ing ev - ery -
snow - - ing, it's snow - ing ev - ery -
win - - dy, it's win - dy ev - ery -
fog - - gy, it's fog - gy ev - ery -

The Plumber Song

Words & Music by
Alison Hedger

Bright and rhythmic ♩ = 126

I'm a qual - i - fied plumb - er, here to help with my bag of tools; you can watch and co - py all the things I've learnt to do.

Last time to Coda

Can I Help You?

Words & Music by
Mark and Helen Johnson

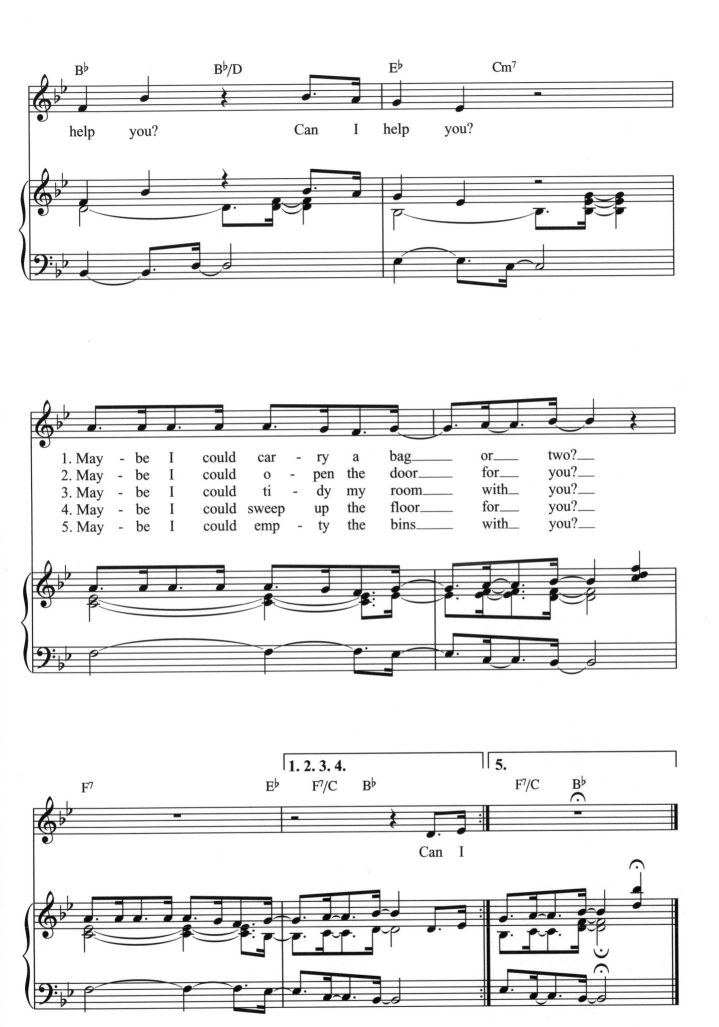

Seasonal Song Collections

by Niki Davies

From one of Britain's top music writers for children, this series of seasonal collections from Niki Davies provides a wonderful library of songs that are simple to learn and great fun to sing – an ideal resource for use throughout the year!

Written for nursery and reception aged children, but suitable for older children too, each book contains ten songs along with lots of ideas for further activities and curriculum links.

Each songbook package provides:

- Quality recordings of all the songs, sung by children
- Professionally arranged and produced backing tracks
- Piano music with melody, lyrics and guitar chords
- Teachers' notes/curriculum links for The Foundation Stage

It Must Be Spring!

With ten brand new songs for spring-time and other times of the year, this songbook will be an instant hit with younger children.

Titles include:

- It must be spring!
- Somebody's waking up
- It's Mother's Day
- Wet, wet, wet!
- Where did the pancake go?
- A tiny seed was sleeping

Happy Sun High

A superb collection of songs for summer and throughout the year, this book includes ten enchanting songs to brighten up everyone's day whatever the weather!

Titles include:

- Come with me to the beach
- Sunglasses
- Caterpillar
- Steam train
- Picnic
- Lying in the daisies

It's Time To Fly

Children will adore these ten original songs for autumn, with words and melodies that beautifully capture the changes of the season.

Titles include:

- One, two, three little acorns
- The owl
- Pumpkin head
- Mr Scarecrow
- Autumn leaves
- Under the harvest moon

It's Winter Time

Providing plenty of material for those winter days, with songs about frosty mornings, keeping warm and Christmas preparations, this book is an ideal supplementary resource for any winter term projects.

Titles include:

- Marching in the snow
- Snowdrop
- Put your coat on
- Jack Frost
- Mister Wind
- Socks

Out of the Ark Music

Out of the Ark Music, Sefton House, 2 Molesey Road, Hersham Green, Surrey KT12 4RQ, UK
Telephone 01932 232250, Fax 01932 703010
Email info@outoftheark.com
www.outoftheark.com